Graphing
GRADE 4

Written by
Vicky Shiotsu

Illustrated by
Becky Radtke

Cover Illustration
by Susan Cumbow

FS112038 Graphing Grade 4
All rights reserved—Printed in the U.S.A.

Copyright © 1999 Frank Schaffer Publications, Inc.
23740 Hawthorne Blvd.
Torrance, CA 90505

TABLE OF CONTENTS

INTRODUCTION

This book has been designed to help students succeed in math. It is part of the *Math Minders* series that provides students with opportunities to practice math skills that they will use throughout their lives.

The activities in this book have been created to help students feel confident about working with graphs. The beginning pages review concepts introduced in earlier grades; the pages gradually increase in difficulty as students learn new concepts and acquire more sophisticated graphing skills. Vocabulary is kept at a fourth-grade level to help ensure student success.

Various formats are used throughout the book to help maintain student interest. Students will be able to progress at their own speed, using the skill learned in one activity to advance to the next level of understanding. The concepts presented in this book can be taught in the classroom or at home. Students will practice a variety of skills, such as reading different kinds of graphs (picture graph, bar graph, circle graph, line graph, coordinate graph), collecting data, and recording information on graphs.

Graphing
GRADE 4

Name_____

Juicy Sales ....

A **picture graph** uses pictures as symbols to show information.

Hank's Market sells several kinds of fruit juice. This picture graph shows how many bottles of juice were sold last Friday.

Bottles of Juice Sold on Friday

apple	🍶🍶🍶🍶🍶🍶🍶🍶
cranberry	🍶🍶🍶🍶🍶🍶
grape	🍶🍶🍶
grapefruit	🍶🍶🍶🍶
orange	🍶🍶🍶🍶🍶🍶🍶

🍶 = 5 bottles of juice

Use the picture graph to answer the questions.

A. How many bottles of juice does each 🍶 in the graph stand for? _____

B. How many bottles of orange juice were sold? _____

C. How many bottles of cranberry juice were sold? _____

D. Which juice was sold the most? _____

E. Which juice was sold the least? _____

F. Which juice was sold more—orange juice or grapefruit juice? _____

G. How many more bottles of cranberry juice were sold than grape juice? _____

H. How many bottles of juice were sold altogether? _____

Graphing Grade 4

Name_____

A **bar graph** uses bars to show numerical information.

Alyssa kept track of the amount of time she spent on homework in a week. She recorded the results on a bar graph.

Time Spent on Homework

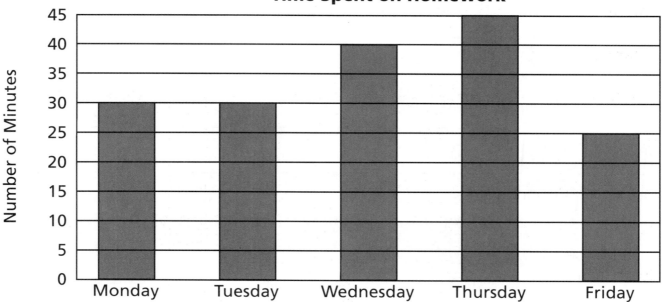

Use the bar graph to answer the questions.

A. How many minutes did Alyssa spend on homework on Wednesday? _____

B. How many minutes did Alyssa spend on homework on Thursday? _____

C. On which two days did she spend the same amount of time on homework?

_____

D. On which day did she spend the most time doing homework?_____

E. On which day did she spend 25 minutes on homework? _____

F. How much more time did she spend doing homework on Wednesday than on Friday?_____

G. How much time did Alyssa spend doing homework altogether during the week?

_____

Name_____

The bar graph below compares the lengths of some fish that live in the ocean.

Fish Lengths in Feet

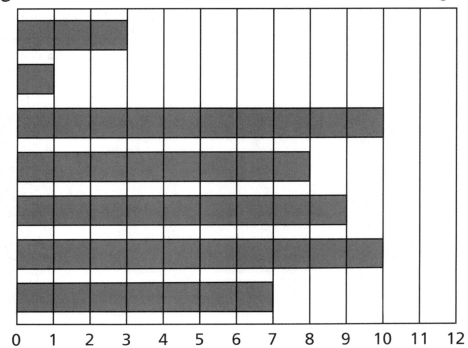

Use the bar graph to answer the questions.

A. Which fish is the smallest? _____
How long is it? _____

B. How long is a bull shark? _____

C. Which is longer—a swordfish or a sailfish? _____

D. Which is longer—a bluefin tuna or a bull shark? _____

E. How many feet longer is a Pacific halibut than an Atlantic cod? _____

F. Which two fish are the same length? _____

G. Which fish are longer than 7 feet? _____

_____

Counting Students ....

Solving word problems/Picture graph

The graph shows how many students attend Learnwell School.

Number of Students at Learnwell School

Kindergarten	🚶 🚶 🚶 🚶 🚶 🚶
1st Grade	🚶 🚶 🚶 🚶 🚶
2nd Grade	🚶 🚶 🚶 🚶 🚶 🚶 🚶
3rd Grade	🚶 🚶 🚶 🚶 🚶 🚶
4th Grade	🚶 🚶 🚶 🚶 🚶 🚶 🚶 🚶
5th Grade	🚶 🚶 🚶 🚶 🚶 🚶

🚶 = 10 students

Use the picture graph to answer the questions.

A. How many students are in kindergarten? _____

B. Are there more students in second grade or third grade? _____

C. Which grade has the fewest students? _____

D. Which grade has the most students? _____

E. How many more students are in fourth grade than in fifth grade? _____

F. How many students are there altogether in fourth and fifth grades? _____

G. Learnwell School has three kindergarten classes. The classes are the same size. How many students are in each class? _____

H. There are two fifth grade classes. One class has two more students than the other. How many students are in each of the fifth grade classes? _____

Name_____

Many Languages .... Solving word problems/Bar graph

Did you know that there are thousands of languages?
This graph lists some of the major ones and the number
of people who speak them.

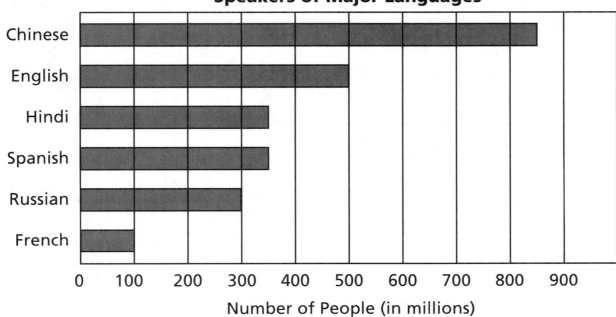

Speakers of Major Languages

Number of People (in millions)

Use the bar graph to answer the questions.

A. Which language is spoken by the most number of people? _____
About how many people speak this language? _____

B. Which two languages are spoken by about the same number of people?

_____

C. About how many people speak English? _____

D. Do more people speak French or Russian? _____

E. Hindi is spoken in India. About how many people speak it? _____

F. Arabic is spoken in the Middle East and northern Africa. Almost twice as many
people speak Arabic than French. About how many people speak Arabic?

_____

Name_____

A Colorful Blanket ....

A **circle graph** displays information on a circle that is divided into sections.

Colors of Felt Squares

Fran sewed eight felt squares together to make a blanket for her doll. This graph shows the different colors of squares she used. Each section of the graph stands for one felt square.

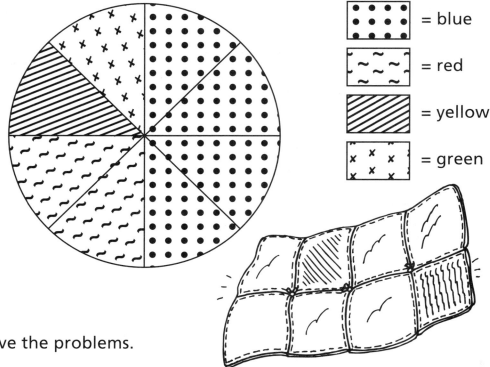

Use the circle graph to solve the problems.

A. How many squares of each color did Fran use?

blue _____   red _____   yellow _____   green _____

B. Which fraction shows how much of the blanket was green— $\frac{1}{2}$, $\frac{1}{4}$, or $\frac{1}{8}$? _____

C. Which fraction shows how much of the blanket was yellow— $\frac{1}{2}$, $\frac{1}{4}$, or $\frac{1}{8}$? _____

D. Which fraction shows how much of the blanket was red— $\frac{2}{4}$, $\frac{2}{6}$, or $\frac{2}{8}$? _____
What is another fraction you could use to show how many of the squares were red— $\frac{1}{2}$, $\frac{1}{3}$, or $\frac{1}{4}$? _____

E. Which fraction shows how much of the blanket was blue— $\frac{2}{4}$, $\frac{2}{6}$, or $\frac{4}{8}$? _____
What is another fraction you could use to show how many of the squares were blue— $\frac{1}{2}$, $\frac{1}{3}$, or $\frac{1}{4}$? _____

Name_____

Evan woke up at 8:00 a.m. and went to bed at 8:00 p.m. This circle graph shows how Evan spent his day. Each section of the graph stands for 1 hour.

How Evan Spent His Day

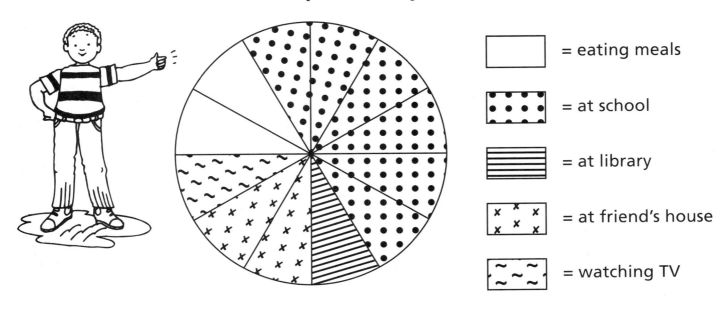

☐ = eating meals

▪ = at school

☰ = at library

✕ = at friend's house

〰 = watching TV

Use the circle graph to answer the questions.

A. How many hours did Evan spend at school? _____

B. How many hours did Evan spend eating meals? _____

C. Did Evan spend more time at school or at his friend's house? _____

D. What fraction shows how much of Evan's day was spent at school— $\frac{6}{6}$, $\frac{6}{8}$, or $\frac{6}{12}$? _____

What other fraction could you use to describe this— $\frac{1}{2}$, $\frac{1}{6}$, or $\frac{1}{12}$? _____

E. Which fraction describes how much of Evan's day was spent at the library— $\frac{1}{2}$, $\frac{1}{6}$, or $\frac{1}{12}$? _____

F. Which fraction describes how much of Evan's day was spent at his friend's house— $\frac{2}{4}$, $\frac{2}{6}$, or $\frac{2}{12}$? _____

What other fraction could you use to describe this— $\frac{1}{2}$, $\frac{1}{3}$, or $\frac{1}{6}$? _____

Name_____

Books for Sale...............................

A **line graph** can show how something changes over time. The dots on the graph below show how a bookstore's sales increased or decreased during the spring and summer months.

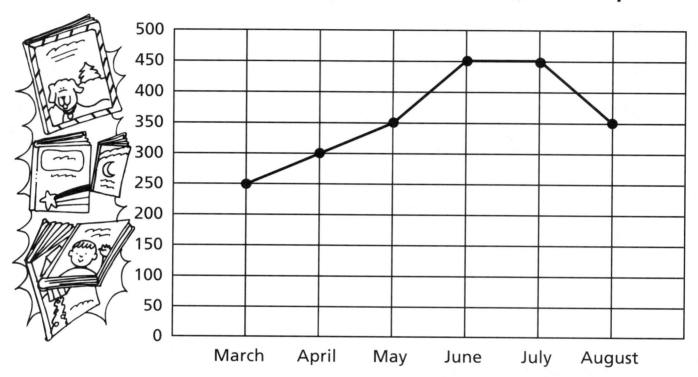

Number of Books Sold at Bookworm's Shop

Use the line graph to answer the questions.

A. How many books were sold in March? _____

B. Did the sales figures increase or decrease from March to April? _____

C. Were more books sold in May than in April? _____

D. How many more books were sold in June than in May? _____

E. What happened to the sales figures from May to June? _____

F. What happened to the sales figures from July to August? _____

G. How many books were sold altogether in July and August? _____

Name_____

At the Movies ....
Solving word problems/Line graph

The science fiction movie "Space Zap" played in theaters for seven weeks.
This graph shows the number of people who saw the movie each week.

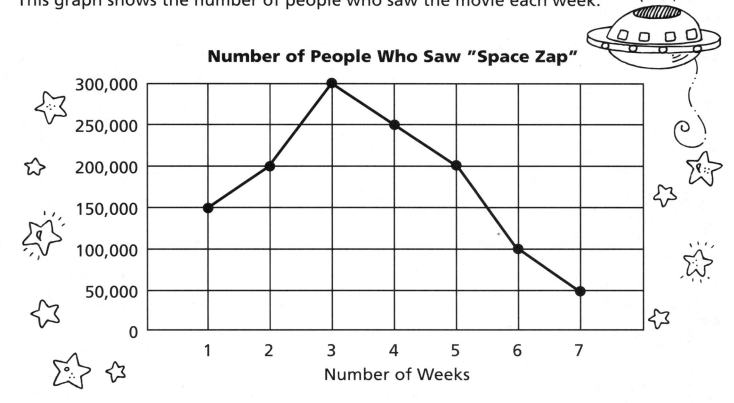

Number of People Who Saw "Space Zap"

Number of Weeks

Use the line graph to answer the questions.

A. How many people saw the movie during its first week in theaters? _____

B. How many people watched the movie during its second week? _____

C. Did the number of viewers increase or decrease from Week 2 to Week 3?

_____

D. In which week was the movie audience the largest? _____

E. In which week was the movie audience the smallest? _____

F. In which week did the number of movie goers begin to decrease? _____

G. How many more people watched the movie during Week 5 than during Week 7?

_____

© Frank Schaffer Publications, Inc.   **11**   Graphing Grade 4

Points on a Map ....

A **coordinate graph** displays information on a grid. A grid is made up of lines that go across and lines that go up and down.

A coordinate graph can help you find things on a map. For example, the grid at the right shows places in a community.

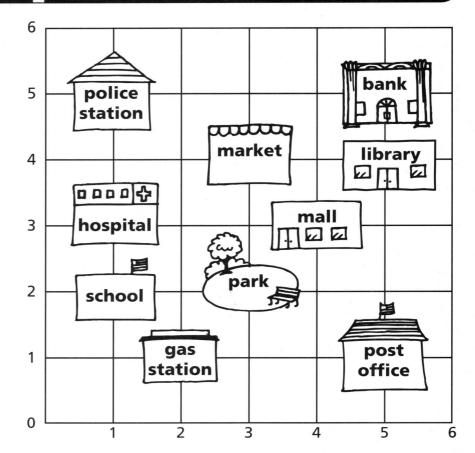

Move along the grid as directed below. Always begin at 0. Then write the place that is at each given location.

A. 1 space across, 2 spaces up _____school_____

B. 5 spaces across, 4 spaces up _____

C. 1 space across, 3 spaces up _____

D. 5 spaces across, 5 spaces up _____

E. 1 space across, 5 spaces up _____

F. 3 spaces across, 4 spaces up _____

G. 5 spaces across, 1 space up _____

H. 4 spaces across, 3 spaces up _____

Where Is It?.................

A number pair can be used to describe a point on a grid. For example, the location of the school on the grid is described by the number pair (2, 4). The numbers show that to find the school, you must move 2 spaces across the grid and 4 spaces up. The first number in the pair shows how many spaces you move across and the second number shows how many spaces you move up.

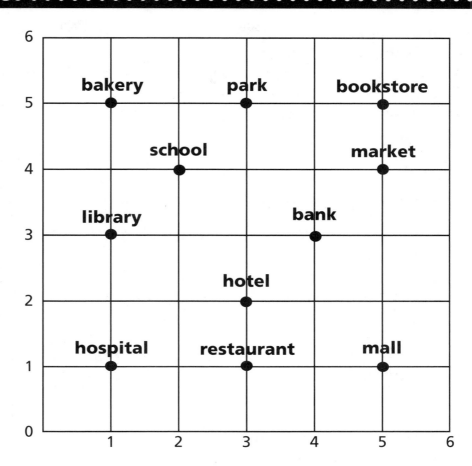

Look at the grid. Write the name of the place that is described by each number pair.

A. (1, 1) _____

B. (3, 2) _____

C. (5, 4) _____

D. (3, 5) _____

E. (1, 3) _____

F. (5, 5) _____

G. (5, 1) _____

H. (3, 1) _____

I. (4, 3) _____

J. (1, 5) _____

Name_____

Tasty Burgers ....

The Hamburger Hut is famous for its tasty burgers. Read the clues below and answer the questions. Then complete the picture graph to show how many hamburgers were served at the Hut in one week.

A. There were 50 more burgers sold on Tuesday than on Monday. How many burgers were sold on Tuesday? _____

B. Twice as many burgers were sold on Friday than on Tuesday. How many burgers were sold on Friday? _____

C. Wednesday's sales were the same as Monday's. How many burgers were sold on Wednesday? _____

D. The total number of burgers sold on Tuesday and Wednesday equals the number sold on Thursday. How many burgers were sold on Thursday? _____

E. There were 100 more burgers sold on Saturday than on Friday. How many burgers were sold on Saturday? _____

F. There were 50 fewer burgers sold on Sunday than on Saturday. How many burgers were sold on Sunday? _____

Hamburger Sales in a Week

Monday	⬤ ⬤ ⬤
Tuesday	
Wednesday	
Thursday	
Friday	
Saturday	
Sunday	

 = 50 hamburgers

　　　　　　　Graphing Grade 4

Name_____

Making Music..................

Mr. Allen is a music teacher. He teaches students how to play various instruments.

Read the clues and answer the questions. Then complete the bar graph to show the number of students who are learning to play each type of instrument.

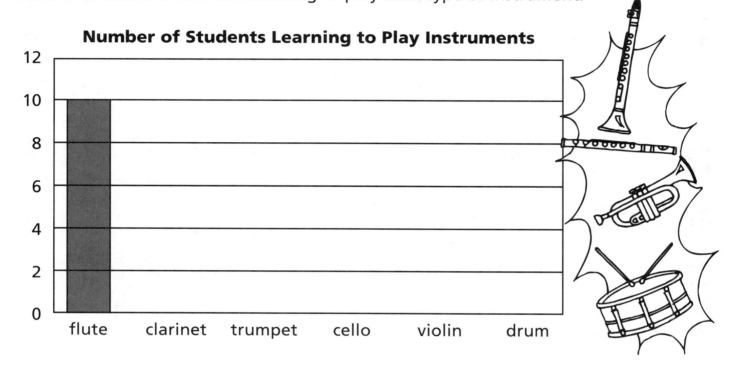

Number of Students Learning to Play Instruments

(Bar graph with y-axis labeled 0, 2, 4, 6, 8, 10, 12 and x-axis labeled: flute, clarinet, trumpet, cello, violin, drum. The flute bar is filled to 10.)

A. There are 4 fewer clarinet players than flute players. How many students play the clarinet? _____

B. Twice as many students play the trumpet than the clarinet. How many students play the trumpet? _____

C. There are 2 fewer students who play the violin than the flute. How many students play the violin? _____

D. There are half as many students who play the drum than there are who play the trumpet. How many students play the drum? _____

E. There are 3 times as many students who play the trumpet than there are who play the cello. How many students play the cello? _____

F. How many students does Mr. Allen teach in all? _____

A Fabric Sale ....

Fantasy Fabrics had a clearance sale. Mrs. Lee bought 8 yards of fabric. She bought 4 different kinds of fabric—dotted, striped, checked, and plain. Read the clues and figure out how much Mrs. Lee bought of each fabric. Write your answers on the chart at the right.

Fabric	Yards Bought
dotted	
striped	
checked	
plain	

Clues:

 Mrs. Lee bought the same amount of dotted and plain fabric.

 Half of the fabric bought was striped.

Mrs. Lee bought twice as much striped fabric than checked fabric.

Fabric Bought

Now use the information from your chart to create a circle graph. Decorate the sections of the circle to match the color key and to show how many yards Mrs. Lee bought of each fabric.

 = dotted   = checked

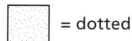 = striped   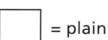 = plain

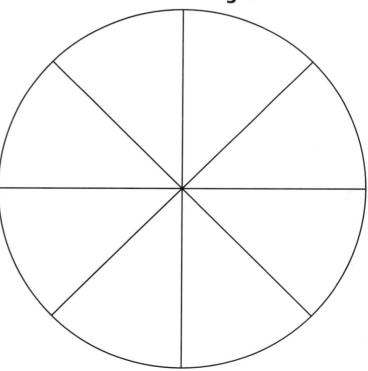

Graphing Grade 4

Name_____

The chart at the right shows the number of computers sold at five computer stores last week. Use the chart to complete the picture graph below.

Computer Store	Number of Computers Sold
Classy Computers	45
Computer Corral	40
Cyberspace Place	50
E-Z Electronics	30
Keyboard Connections	25

Number of Computers Sold

Classy Computers	
Computer Corral	
Cyberspace Place	
E-Z Electronics	
Keyboard Connections	

■ = 5 computers

Look at the picture graph and answer the questions.

A. Which store sold the most computers?_____

B. Which store sold the fewest computers? _____

C. How many more computers were sold at Computer Corral than at E-Z Electronics? _____

D. Which store sold more—Classy Computers or Computer Corral?

_____

Name_____

Famous Rivers .... Using data from a chart to make a bar graph

The chart at the right gives the approximate lengths of some famous rivers. Use the chart to complete the bar graph below.

River	Length (in miles)
Amazon	4,000
Congo	3,000
Ganges	1,500
Mackenzie	1,000
Mississippi	2,500
Nile	4,000
Seine	500

Lengths of Rivers (in miles)

Amazon								
Congo								
Ganges								
Mackenzie								
Mississippi								
Nile								
Seine								

0   500   1,000   1,500   2,000   2,500   3,000   3,500   4,000

Look at the bar graph and answer the questions.

A. Which two rivers are the longest in the world? _____

B. The Seine flows through Paris, France. About how long is it? _____

C. The Mackenzie is Canada's longest river. About how long is it? _____

D. Is Africa's Congo River 2 or 3 times longer than the Mackenzie? _____

E. The Mississippi is the longest river in the United States. About how many miles longer is it than Bangladesh and India's Ganges River? _____

Name_____

A Color Survey ....

Joe asked 12 people to name their favorite color. He wrote their answers on a chart.

Color	Number of People
blue	3
green	1
orange	1
purple	2
red	4
yellow	1

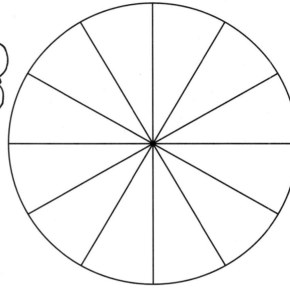

Use the chart to create a circle graph.
First, color the key. Then color each
section of the circle to match the
information on the chart.

☐ = blue   ☐ = purple

☐ = green   ☐ = red

☐ = orange   ☐ = yellow

Look at the circle graph and answer the questions.

A. Which color did most people like the best? _____
How many chose that color? _____

B. How many people picked blue as their favorite color? _____

C. Did more people like green or purple? _____

D. What fraction shows how many people liked yellow the best? _____

E. What fraction shows how many people liked purple the best? _____

F. What fraction shows how many people liked blue the best? _____

G. What fraction shows how many people liked red the best? _____

Winter Lows

The chart shows Chillyville's daily low temperatures during one week in January.

Use the information on the chart to make a line graph. First, plot the temperatures by making a dot for each day. Then connect the dots together with straight lines. Look at the line graph and answer the questions at the bottom of the page.

Day	Low Temperatures (in degrees Fahrenheit)
Mon.	15
Tues.	12
Wed.	15
Thurs.	21
Fri.	24
Sat.	21
Sun.	18

Daily Low Temperatures

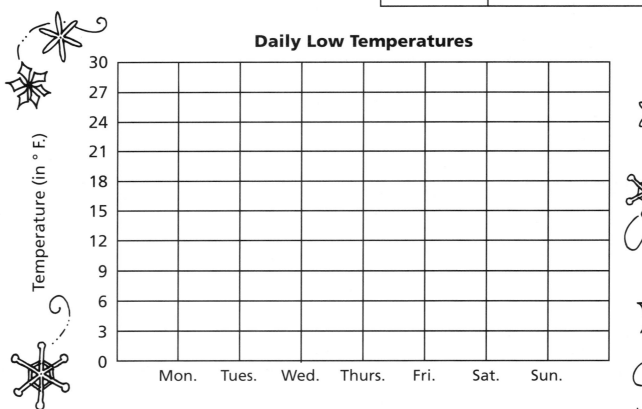

A. Which day got the coldest? _____

B. Which day got the warmest? _____

C. Was Saturday's low temperature higher or lower than Sunday's? _____

Name_____

Graph a Shape ....

Read the number pairs. Graph the points on the grid.
Make a check mark beside the number pair after you plot
the point on the grid. When all the points are on the
grid, connect them in the order listed to see a shape.

(5, 8) ✓_____   (2, 4) _____   (4, 2) _____   (6, 2) _____   (8, 4) _____

(3, 6) ✓_____   (3, 4) _____   (4, 1) _____   (9, 2) _____   (6, 6) _____

(4, 6) _____   (1, 2) _____   (6, 1) _____   (7, 4) _____   (7, 6) _____

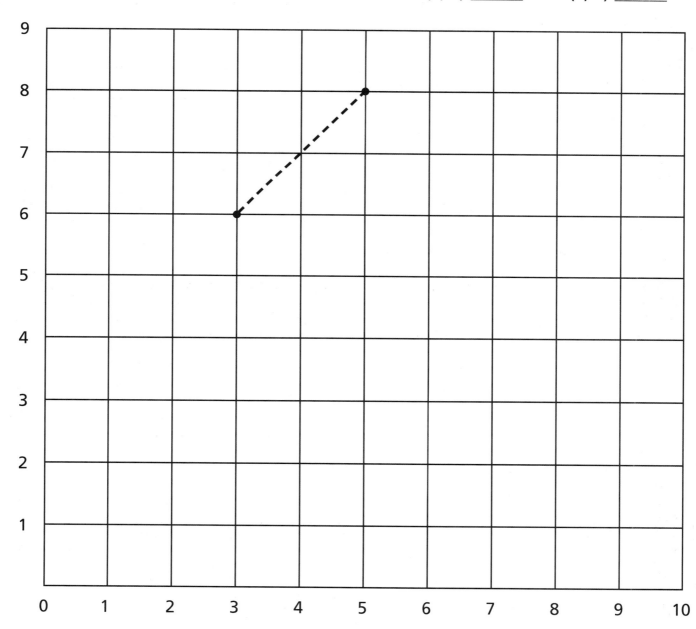

Name_____

Name the Points ....

Greg plotted some points on a grid. He labeled each point with a letter. Look at the number pairs below. They identify points on the grid. Write the letter you find at each point.

A. (1, 7) _____

B. (4, 5) _____

C. (7, 1) _____

D. (5, 6) _____

E. (2, 3) _____

F. (6, 4) _____

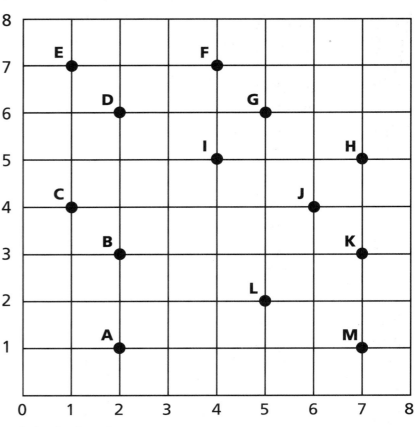

Write the number pair for each of the labeled points.

G. D _____   **H.** A _____   **I.** C _____   **J.** L _____

K. H _____   **L.** K _____   **M.** J _____   **N.** I _____

Plot some points on the grid and connect them so that they form a letter. Write the number pairs that describe the point you used. An example is done for you.

V — (1, 7), (2, 4), (3, 7)

_____

_____

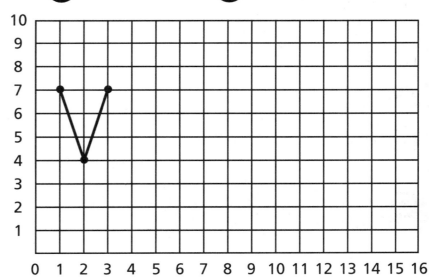

A Choice of Graphs......

Sometimes you can use different graphs to give the same information. For example, look at the bar graph. It shows how the population of Boomtown grew over the years.

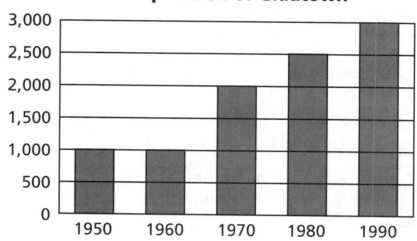

Population of Gladtown

Now use the bar graph to make a line graph showing the same information.

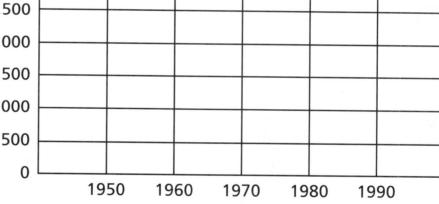

Look at both graphs. Answer the questions.

A. Do both graphs help you see how the population changed over the years? _____

B. Which graph do you prefer? _____ Why? _____
_____

C. Would a circle graph work well to show the same information? Why or why not?
_____
_____

Kinds of Graphs ....

Choosing the most appropriate graph

There are many kinds of graphs. Examples of some are shown at the right. When you are trying to decide what kind of graph to use, think about what kind of display would give the clearest information.

Bottles of Juice Sold on Friday

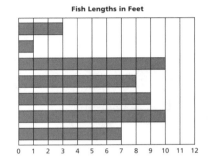

 = 5 bottles of juice

picture graph

Write which type of graph you would choose to show the following information.

A. You want to show the 10 highest mountains in the world.

_____

bar graph

Fish Lengths in Feet

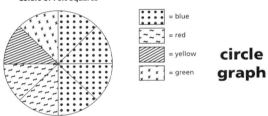

B. You plan to keep a record of how tall your bean plant grows.

_____

C. There are 24 students in your class. You want to show what fraction of the class has pets and what fraction does not.

_____

Colors of Felt Squares

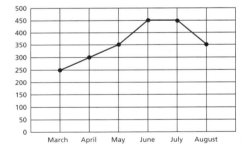

= blue
= red
= yellow
= green

circle graph

D. You are going to graph the heights of the people in your family.

_____

Number of Books Sold at Bookworm's Shop

line graph

E. You want to graph your neighbors' houses to show where they are in location to your home.

_____

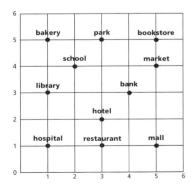

coordinate graph

F. You are studying the world's population growth. You want to show how often the population doubles.

_____

Graphing Grade 4

Pretty Bouquets ················

Gathering data from two graphs

Sue and Craig each picked a bouquet of flowers for their mothers. Each child picked 12 flowers. The circle graphs show what kinds of flowers they put in their bouquets.

Sue's Bouquet

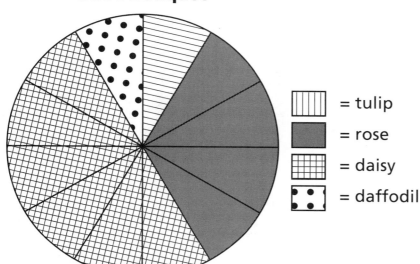

Craig's Bouquet

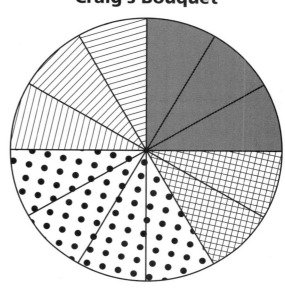

||||| = tulip

▓ = rose

▦ = daisy

⠿ = daffodil

Look at both graphs to help you answer the questions.

A. How many tulips did Sue pick? _____

B. How many tulips did Craig pick? _____

C. Did Sue pick more roses or daisies? _____

D. Did Craig pick more roses or daisies? _____

E. Who picked the most daffodils? _____

F. Who picked the most tulips? _____

G. What fraction shows how much of Sue's bouquet was made up of roses? _____

H. What fraction shows how much of Craig's bouquet was made up of roses? _____

Name_____

Newsworthy Graphs .... Gathering data from two graphs

The Local Times and *The Jolly Journal* are owned by two
different newspaper companies. The graphs below show how
many copies each company sold during a five-week period.

Sales for *The Local Times*

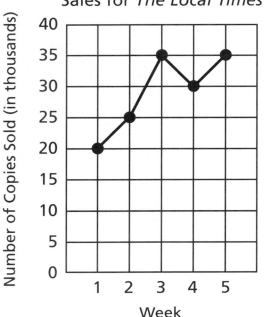

Sales for *The Jolly Journal*

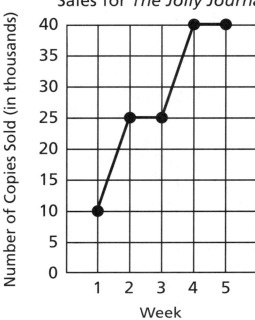

Look at both graphs to help you answer the questions.

A. Which newspaper sold more copies during Week 1? _____

B. During which week did both newspapers sell the same amount? _____

C. How many copies of *The Local Times* were sold altogether in the first three
weeks? _____

D. How many copies of *The Jolly Journal* were sold altogether in the first three
weeks? _____

E. During which weeks did *The Jolly Journal* sell more copies than *The Local Times*?
_____

F. Which newspaper sold the most copies at the end of the five-week period?
_____

Graphing Grade 4

Name_____

Stuck on Stamps............

Make a picture graph showing how many stamps come in your mail in one week.

1. Look through Monday's mail. Count how many stamps you find. Record the number on a sheet of paper.
2. Repeat step 1 for the next four days.
3. Look at the graph below. List the days in the left-hand column.
4. Think of a symbol you can use to stand for one stamp. Draw the symbol below the graph. Draw the correct number of stamps for each day.

Number of Stamps in the Mail

= 1 stamp

Look at the completed graph. Answer the questions.

A. On which day did you find the most stamps? _____
How many stamps did you find that day? _____

B. On which day did you find the least number of stamps? _____
How many stamps did you find that day? _____

C. How many stamps did you find in all? _____

D. Suppose you wanted to make another graph showing the kinds of pictures featured on the stamps. For example, you might show that some stamps featured people while others displayed plants. What kind of graph would you use? _____

Name_____

Birthday Survey ....

Make a bar graph showing in which months people celebrate their birthdays.

1. Ask 12 people to name the month in which their birthday falls. Record their answers on a sheet of paper.
2. Count how many people are listed for each month.
3. Color the bars on the graph to match your findings.

Birthdays

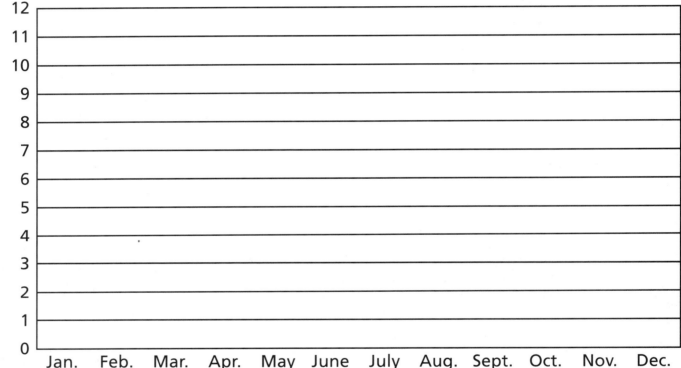

Look at the completed graph. Answer the questions.

A. In which month did most of the birthdays fall? _____

B. Which had more birthdays—the first six months of the year or the last six months? _____

C. In what month is your birthday? _____
Add that information to the chart. How many people on the graph have the same birthday month as yours? _____

Name_____

Throw the Die........................

Make a circle graph showing how a die lands when you toss it.

How a Die Landed When Tossed

1. Toss a die 12 times. Each time record which number lands facing up.
2. Color the rectangles in the key below. Color the circle graph to match your findings.

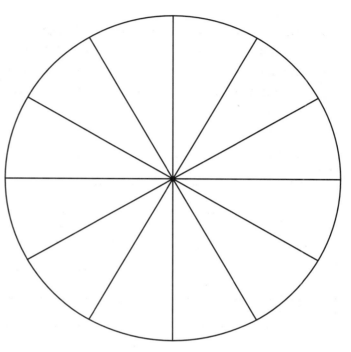

☐ = 1   ☐ = 4

☐ = 2   ☐ = 5

☐ = 3   ☐ = 6

Look at the completed graph and write the answers.

A. Which number landed face up most often? _____

B. Which number landed face up the least number of times? _____

C. Write a fraction showing how much of the time the numbers 1 to 6 appeared face up:

1 _____   2 _____   3 _____   4 _____   5 _____   6 _____

D. Compare your graph with that of another student. Were the results similar or different? Explain your answer.

_____

_____

Name_____

Make a line graph showing how many minutes of reading you do in a week.

1. Keep track of how many minutes you read for pleasure each day. (This can include reading library books, magazines, comic books, and letters.) Write the minutes on a sheet of paper. Do this for one week.
2. Record your findings on the graph below. Write the dates on the lines. For each day, draw a dot where the lines for the number of minutes and the day meet.
3. Connect the dots with a ruler.

Number of Minutes I Read

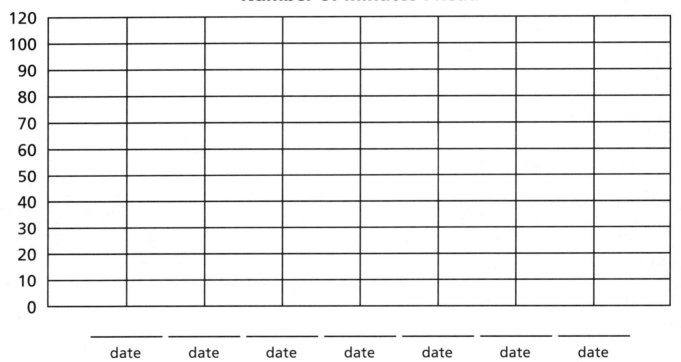

| date | date | date | date | date | date | date |

Look at the completed graph. Answer the questions.

A. On which day did you spend the most time reading? _____

B. On which day did you spend the least amount of time reading? _____

C. How many minutes did you read altogether that week? _____

ANSWERS

Page 3
A. 5
B. 35
C. 30
D. apple juice
E. grape juice
F. orange juice
G. 15
H. 140

Page 4
A. 40
B. 45
C. Monday, Tuesday
D. Thursday
E. Friday
F. 15 minutes
G. 170 minutes

Page 5
A. Atlantic herring, 1 foot
B. 8 feet
C. sailfish
D. bluefin tuna
E. 6 feet
F. bluefin tuna, sailfish
G. bluefin tuna, bull shark, Pacific halibut, sailfish

Page 6
A. 60
B. 2nd grade
C. 1st grade
D. 4th grade
E. 20
F. 140
G. 20
H. 31, 29

Page 7
A. Chinese, 850 million
B. Hindi and Spanish
C. 500 million
D. Russian
E. 350 million
F. 200 million

Page 8
A. blue—4, red—2, yellow—1, green—1
B. 1/8
C. 1/8
D. 2/8, 1/4
E. 4/8, 1/2

Page 9
A. 6
B. 2
C. at school
D. 6/12, 1/2
E. 1/12
F. 2/12, 1/6

Page 10
A. 250
B. increase
C. yes
D. 100
E. increased
F. decreased
G. 800

Page 11
A. 150,000
B. 200,000
C. increase
D. Week 3
E. Week 7
F. Week 4
G. 150,000

Page 12
A. school
B. library
C. hospital
D. bank
E. police station
F. market
G. post office
H. mall

Page 13
A. hospital
B. hotel
C. market
D. park
E. library
F. bookstore
G. mall
H. restaurant
I. bank
J. bakery

Page 14
Graph should be completed as shown:

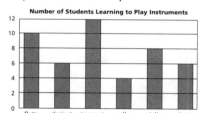

A. 200
B. 400
C. 150
D. 350
E. 500
F. 450

Page 15
A. 6
B. 12
C. 8
D. 6
E. 4
F. 46
Graph should be completed as shown:

Page 16
Chart should be completed to show the following:
dotted – 1 yard bought
striped – 4 yards bought
checked – 2 yards bought
plain – 1 yard bought
Graph should be completed as shown:

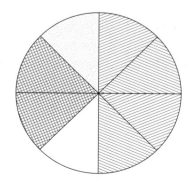

Graphing Grade 4

ANSWERS

Page 17
Graph should be completed as shown:

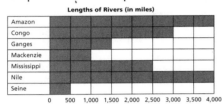

A. Cyberspace Place
B. Keyboard Connections
C. 10
D. Classy Computers

Page 18
Graph should be completed as shown:

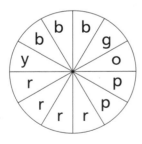

A. Amazon, Nile
B. 500 miles
C. 1,000 miles
D. 3 times
E. 1,000 miles

Page 19
Graph should be completed as shown:

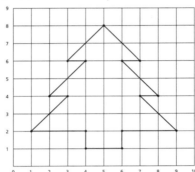

A. red, 4
B. 3
C. purple
D. 1/12
E. 2/12 or 1/6
F. 3/12 or 1/4
G. 4/12 or 1/3

Page 20
Graph should be completed as shown:

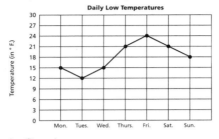

A. Tuesday
B. Friday
C. higher

Page 21
Grid should be completed as shown:

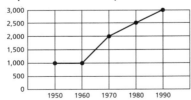

Page 22
A. E   H. (2, 1)
B. I   I. (1, 4)
C. M   J. (5, 2)
D. G   K. (7, 5)
E. B   L. (7, 3)
F. J   M. (6, 4)
G. (2, 6)   N. (4, 5)
Students' grids will vary.

Page 23
Graph should be completed as shown:

A. yes
B. Answer varies.
C. A circle graph would not work as well
   because it doesn't display changes that
   occur over a period of time very well.

Page 24
Accept all reasonable answers.

Page 25
A. 1
B. 3
C. daisies
D. roses
E. Craig
F. Craig
G. 4/12 or 1/3
H. 3/12 or 1/4

Page 26
A. The Local Times
B. Week 2
C. 80,000
D. 60,000
E. Weeks 4 and 5
F. The Local Times

Page 27
Graph will vary.
A. Answers will vary.
B. Answers will vary.
C. Answer will vary.
D. Answer will vary.

Page 28
Graph will vary.
A. Answer will vary.
B. Answer will vary.
C. Answers will vary.

Page 29
Graph will vary.
A. Answer will vary.
B. Answer will vary.
C. Answers will vary.
D. Answer will vary.

Page 30
Graph will vary.
A. Answer will vary.
B. Answer will vary.
C. Answer will vary.